French

Helpful hints for parents

- Start at the beginning of the book and try to work through the activities in order.
- Encourage your child to work independently as much as possible, without referring to the answers!
- Discuss any areas that your child finds particularly tricky and don't worry if he or she finds any of the exercises too difficult. Remember, children learn different things at different rates.
- Give help and lots of praise, rewarding your child by adding stickers to the reward certificate for great work and effort.
- Once you have completed the workbook, move on to the practice pages bound in the centre.

Autumn
Publishing
www.autumnchildrensbooks.co.uk

How do you say...?

Learn how to say the sounds of the letters. If you don't know how to say a word you can follow the pronunciation guide set within the brackets.

Vowels

a (as in b**a**t) for **salon** (salohn)

à (as in **a**nt) for **là** (la)

â (as in p**a**sta) for **pâtes** (paht)

é (as in caf**e**) for **marché** (marshay)

è (as in **e**gg) for **père** (pear)

i (as in f**i**eld) for **il** (eel)

î (as in f**i**ll) for **île** (eeluh)

o (as in g**o**t) for **bon** (bohn)

ô (as in **o**val) for **hôtel** (ohtel)

oe (as 'ir' in b**ir**d) for **soeur** (sir)

u (as in r**u**de) for r**ue** (roo)

ù (as in t**u**be) for **où** (ooh)

Nasal sounds

These nasal sounds are pronounced 'through the nose'. Look out for them when a vowel appears before an 'n'.

ans (ahn)

médecin (maydesan)

bon (bohn)

un (un)

chien (sheyan)

Consonants

French consonants are pronounced more clearly than English consonants, e.g. the 'r' is 'rolled' at the back of the mouth. However, there are some exceptions: 'h' is never pronounced.

homme (om)

hôtel (ohtel)

JE SUIS UN CHIEN.
I AM A DOG.

Syllables

In English, we tend to stress the first part of a word and then 'slur' the remaining syllables, whereas in French, the last syllable is stressed. Try it:

professeur (pro-fess-ur)

conversation (con-ver-sas-iyon)

médecin (may-de-san)

Male and female nouns

In French, nouns (i.e. people, places and things) are either masculine (**un** or **le**) or feminine (**une** or **la**).

For example:

Masculine
un chien – a dog
le chien – the dog

A French dictionary will tell you whether a noun is masculine or feminine.

Feminine
une maison – a house
la maison – the house

Plurals

Add **'s'** to the noun unless it ends in **s**, **x** or **z** in which case there is no change.

Add **'x'** when the noun ends in **eau** and **eu**.

For example:
un fils, les fils – son, sons
un gâteau, les gâteaux – cake, cakes

Nombres

Numbers

Knowing your numbers is important because we use numbers in many ways, e.g. to tell the time, to pay for things, to know our house or our phone number, and to know when our birthday is! Learn the following numbers:

GET IT?

32 is **trente-deux**, 33 is **trente-trois**… 41 is **quarante et un**, 42 is **quarante-deux**… and so on.

0	zéro	**11**	onze	**21**	vingt et un	**31**	trente et un…
1	un / une	**12**	douze	**22**	vingt-deux	**40**	quarante
2	deux	**13**	treize	**23**	vingt-trois	**50**	cinquante
3	trois	**14**	quatorze	**24**	vingt-quatre	**60**	soixante
4	quatre	**15**	quinze	**25**	vingt-cinq	**70**	soixante-dix
5	cinq	**16**	seize	**26**	vingt-six	**80**	quatre-vingts
6	six	**17**	dix-sept	**27**	vingt-sept	**90**	quatre-vingt-dix
7	sept	**18**	dix-huit	**28**	vingt-huit	**100**	cent
8	huit	**19**	dix-neuf	**29**	vingt-neuf	**101**	cent un
9	neuf	**20**	vingt	**30**	trente	**200**	deux cents
10	dix						

Write in French some memorable numbers here, e.g. your age, birthday, lucky number, etc:

_____

_____

_____

_____

MY LUCKY NUMBER IS 'NEUF'!

Draw a line to join each of these numerals to the correct French word.

9	vingt-huit
15	soixante-dix
28	trente-six
36	neuf
70	quinze

Now write these numerals as French words.

2 _____

11 _____

31 _____

49 _____

80 _____

MY PHONE NUMBER IS **12-33-55-61**
(DOUZE, TRENTE-TROIS, CINQUANTE-CINQ,
SOIXANTE ET UN).

Couleurs

Colours

Learn these useful colours:

orange – orange

marron – brown

rose – pink

rouge – red

jaune – yellow

The colours below can be either masculine or feminine to match the nouns they describe. The 'e' ending matches feminine nouns.

vert / verte – green

bleu / bleue – blue

gris / grise – grey

noir / noire – black

blanc / blanche – white

violet / violette – purple

For example:

une pomme (f) **_rouge_**
– a red apple

une pomme (f) **_verte_**
– a green apple

'Rouge' is both masculine and feminine. This means the ending stays the same – it doesn't need to change with the noun.

Now it's your turn. Colour the pictures below in any colours you choose. Then write the word for the colour that matches your picture.

une casquette (f)

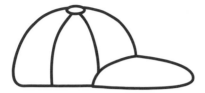

_____

une fleur (f)

_____

un lapin (m)

une banane (f)

_____

un ballon (m)

_____

un gâteau (m)

_____

GET IT?

un = masculine (m)

une = feminine (f)

Les vêtements

Clothes

Colour these clothes in the correct colours.

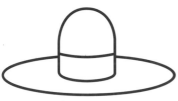

un jean bleu

une jupe jaune

un chapeau noir

les bottes marron

un tee-shirt rouge

GET IT?

Notice the position of the colour word in these French phrases. If you've forgotten the names of the colours, go back to the first *Couleurs* page.

C'EST COMBIEN?
HOW MUCH IS IT?

DE QUELLE COULEUR?
WHAT COLOUR?

BLANC, S'IL VOUS PLAÎT.
WHITE, PLEASE.

Key vocabulary

une boutique – shop
un grand magasin – department store
un rayon de vêtements – clothes department
la taille – size
une carte de crédit – credit card

l'argent – money
les billets – notes
un rabais – discount
un reçu / un ticket de caisse – receipt
un remboursement – a refund

Fit these French words into the crossword grid below. They must fit exactly.
Two words have been done for you.

manteau – coat *(7 letters)*

gants – gloves *(5 letters)*

chaussures – shoes *(10 letters)*

veste – jacket *(5 letters)*

pantalon – trousers *(8 letters)*

collant – tights *(7 letters)*

tricot – cardigan *(6 letters)*

chemise – shirt *(7 letters)*

robe – dress *(4 letters)*

sac – bag *(3 letters)*

C
H
A
U
S
S
U
R
E
S

C
H
E
M
I
S
E

WHAT ARE YOU
WEARING TODAY? SAY
IT IN FRENCH!

Mois de l'année

Months of the year

Find the month in which you were born in the list below.

janvier – January
février – February
mars – March
avril – April
mai – May
juin – June
juillet – July
août – August
septembre – September
octobre – October
novembre – November
décembre – December

IN FRENCH, MONTHS AND DAYS **DON'T** START WITH A CAPITAL LETTER UNLESS THEY ARE AT THE BEGINNING OF A SENTENCE.

If you were born on 1st March you would say:
"le premier mars"

If you were born on 5th July you would say:
"le cinq juillet"

Write the day and month when you were born:

_____

When is Christmas Day?

_____

When is New Year's Day?

_____

25TH DECEMBER

Noël!

1ST JANUARY

Jour de l'An

I WAS BORN ON 20TH MAY. HOW DO I SAY THAT?

Jours de la semaine

Days of the week

Learn to say the days of the week in French.

lundi – Monday
mardi – Tuesday
mercredi – Wednesday
jeudi – Thursday
vendredi – Friday
samedi – Saturday
dimanche – Sunday

Complete the diary entry for today. Write the day, the date and the month. For example:

Day: lundi

Date and month:

le huit août

Day:

Date and month:

QUELLE EST LA DATE
DE TON ANNIVERSAIRE?
WHEN IS YOUR BIRTHDAY?

C'EST LE QUATRE AVRIL.
MY BIRTHDAY IS 4TH APRIL.

Les heures

The time

IL EST UNE HEURE.
IT IS ONE O'CLOCK.

IL EST DEUX HEURES.
IT IS TWO O'CLOCK.

IL EST MIDI.
IT IS MIDDAY.

IL EST MINUIT.
IT IS MIDNIGHT.

IL EST TROIS HEURES.
IT IS THREE O'CLOCK.

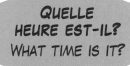

QUELLE HEURE EST-IL?
WHAT TIME IS IT?

ET QUART
QUARTER PAST

ET DEMI(E)
HALF PAST

MOINS LE QUART
QUARTER TO

Draw lines to join the clocks to the times in French.

IL EST SIX HEURES.

IL EST DEUX HEURES ET DEMIE.

IL EST CINQ HEURES ET QUART.

IL EST HUIT HEURES MOINS LE QUART.

IL EST NEUF HEURES.

IL EST DIX HEURES ET DEMIE.

GET IT?

Demi has an 'e' (demie) when it comes after the hours.

La conversation

Let's talk

Learn these basic French words and phrases.

Oui – Yes

Non – No

Salut! – Hello!

Je m'appelle – My name is

Bonjour – Good day

Bonne nuit – Good night

Au revoir – Good bye

À bientôt – See you soon

Ça va? – How are you?

Très bien, merci – Very well, thanks

Merci beaucoup – Thank you very much

Excusez-moi / Pardon – Sorry

Je comprends – I understand

Je ne comprends pas – I don't understand

Je vous en prie – Don't mention it

S'il vous plaît – Please

Parlez-vous anglais? – Do you speak English?

Je parle français – I speak French

PRACTICE MAKES PERFECT

Write the male and female variations of the following colours:

	Masculine	Feminine
green		
blue		
purple		
black		
grey		
white		

Draw a line to match the days in French and English.

vendredi		Tuesday
dimanche	Friday	
mercredi		Monday
mardi	Thursday	
samedi		Saturday
lundi	Sunday	
jeudi		Wednesday

WHAT'S THE TIME?

Write the times in French under the clocks.

A.

B.

C.

D.

E.

F.

FOOD FUN!

Label these fruits.

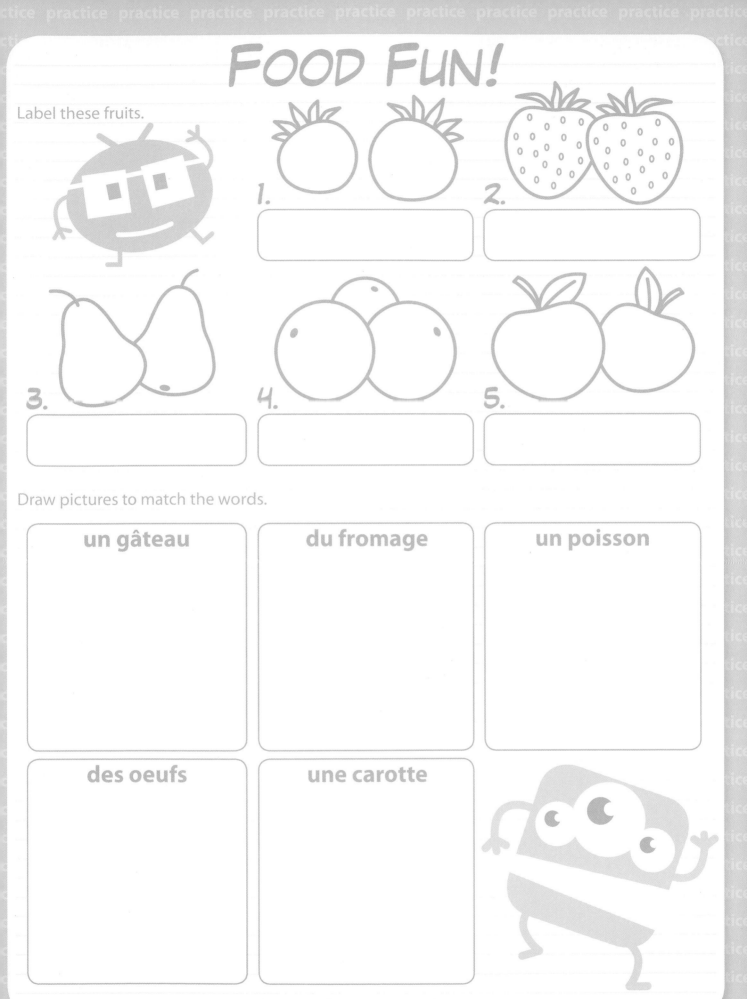

1.

2.

3.

4.

5.

Draw pictures to match the words.

un gâteau

du fromage

un poisson

des oeufs

une carotte

THE BODY

Label the body with the correct French words.

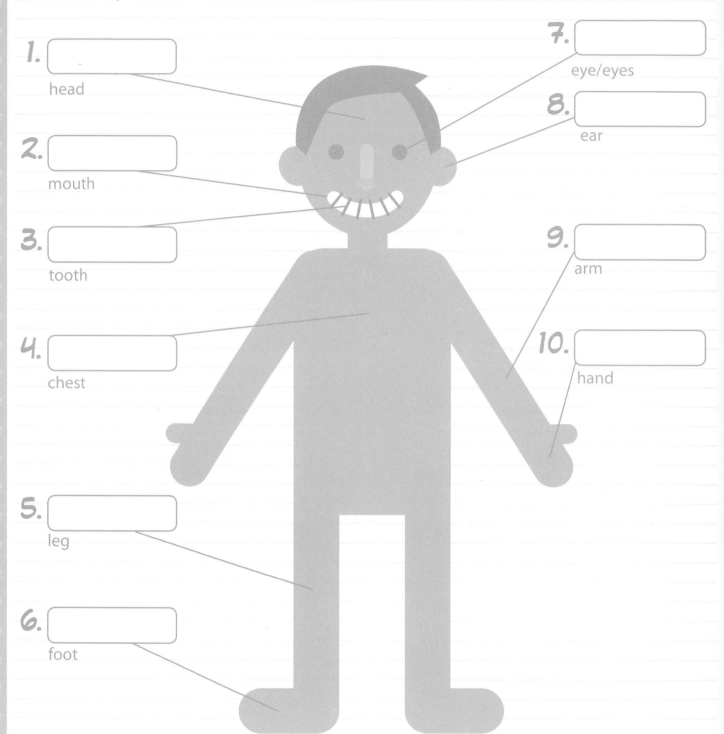

1. [   ]
   head

2. [   ]
   mouth

3. [   ]
   tooth

4. [   ]
   chest

5. [   ]
   leg

6. [   ]
   foot

7. [   ]
   eye/eyes

8. [   ]
   ear

9. [   ]
   arm

10. [   ]
    hand

Now answer these questions.

a. Write 'My chest is hurting' in French. [   ]

b. What does 'Je suis malade' mean? [   ]

Contraires

Opposites

Find the words for these French opposites in the word square.

Look across and down the grid.

grand – big	**ouvert** – open	**rapide** – quick	**premier** – first
petit – small	**fermé** – shut	**lent** – slow	**dernier** – last
chaud – hot	**vrai** – true	**bien** – right	**dehors** – out
froid – cold	**faux** – false	**mal** – wrong	**dans** – in

```
M  T  P  E  T  I  T  S  B  N  M  P
N  R  V  Z  F  W  W  G  R  A  N  D
B  W  V  S  Z  D  E  H  O  R  S  Y
V  G  R  B  P  R  E  M  I  E  R  Y
C  F  A  U  X  P  R  M  V  Z  B  C
X  E  I  L  L  M  N  P  W  J  I  C
O  R  D  E  R  N  I  E  R  Y  E  W
U  M  R  S  W  F  R  M  J  Y  N  L
V  É  G  G  B  R  R  A  P  I  D  E
E  E  H  K  R  O  O  L  H  U  E  N
R  Q  J  N  V  I  L  Z  K  G  B  T
T  C  H  A  U  D  D  A  N  S  W  K
```

La famille

The family

Find the names of people in the family in this word square.

Look across and down the grid.

mère – mother

père – father

fille – daughter

fils – son

sœur – sister

frère – brother

tante – aunt

oncle – uncle

nièce – niece

neveu – nephew

grand-mère – grandmother

grand-père – grandfather

petite-fille – granddaughter

petit-fils – grandson

cousine – female cousin

cousin – male cousin

F	R	T	I	D	L	M	M	N	X	L
G	R	A	N	D	P	È	R	E	L	G
B	O	N	F	Q	P	R	F	F	P	R
N	N	T	I	P	È	E	R	F	E	A
I	C	E	L	U	R	H	È	I	T	N
È	L	P	S	O	E	U	R	L	I	D
C	E	Y	B	T	L	Q	E	L	T	M
E	H	C	O	U	S	I	N	E	F	È
Q	L	N	N	E	V	E	U	Z	I	R
P	E	T	I	T	E	F	I	L	L	E
M	Q	E	C	O	U	S	I	N	S	W

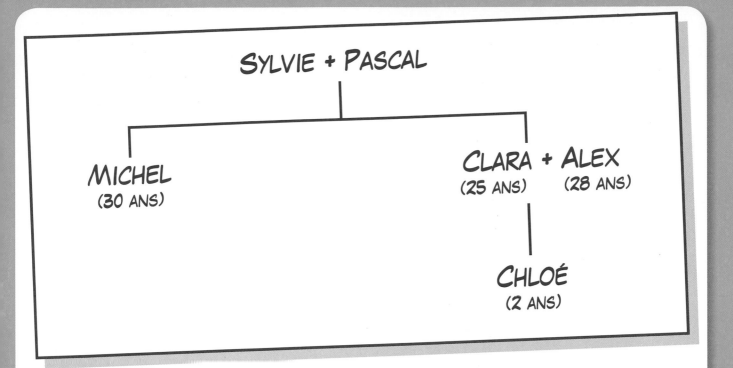

SYLVIE + PASCAL

MICHEL
(30 ANS)

CLARA + ALEX
(25 ANS) (28 ANS)

CHLOÉ
(2 ANS)

Study the family tree. Pretend you are Michel. Complete the sentences below using the following words:

deux   Sylvie   trente   Clara   vingt-cinq   Pascal

1. Je m'appelle Michel. J'ai _____ ans.

2. Ma mère s'appelle _____.

3. Mon père s'appelle _____.

4. Ma sœur s'appelle _____.

5. Clara a _____ ans.

6. Ma nièce, Chloé, a _____ ans.

Toi et moi

You and me

Read the French conversation.

COMMENT T'APPELLES-TU?
WHAT IS YOUR NAME?

JE M'APPELLE KIT.
MY NAME IS KIT.

QUEL ÂGE AS-TU?
HOW OLD ARE YOU?

J'AI NEUF ANS.
I AM 9 YEARS OLD.

TU PEUX TE DÉCRIRE?
CAN YOU DESCRIBE YOURSELF?

J'AI LES YEUX VERTS ET LES CHEVEUX MARRON.
I HAVE GREEN EYES AND BROWN HAIR.

Write a sentence in French to describe what **you** look like!

_____

_____

Key vocabulary

grand/e – tall

petit/e – short

les cheveux longs – long hair

les cheveux courts – short hair

frisés – wavy

les cheveux raides – straight hair

marron – brown

blonds – blond / blonde

roux – auburn

noirs – black

les yeux bleus – blue eyes

les yeux verts – green eyes

GET IT?

I have blond hair.
J'ai les cheveux blonds.

'Hair' is a masculine plural noun so we use masculine plural adjectives.

Get this grammar!

Avoir – to have

J'ai – I have

Tu as – you have (to a friend)

Il / elle a – he, she, it has

Nous avons – we have

Vous avez – you have
(to a stranger, or two or more people)

Ils / elles ont – they have

Être – to be

Je suis – I am

Tu es – you are (to a friend)

Il / elle est – he, she, it is

Nous sommes – we are

Vous êtes – you are
(to a stranger, or two or more people)

Ils / elles sont – they are

TU AS UN FRÈRE OU UNE SOEUR?
DO YOU HAVE A BROTHER OR SISTER?

OUI, J'AI UNE SOEUR.
YES, I HAVE A SISTER.

NON, JE SUIS
FILS/FILLE UNIQUE.
NO, I'M AN ONLY (M/F) CHILD.

OUI, J'AI UN FRÈRE.
YES, I HAVE A BROTHER.

NON, JE N'AI PAS DE FRÈRE.
NO, I DON'T HAVE A BROTHER.

TU AS UN ANIMAL?
DO YOU HAVE A PET?

J'AI UN CHIEN. I HAVE A DOG.
IL S'APPELLE DIG. HIS NAME IS DIG.
IL EST MARRON. HE IS BROWN.

Key vocabulary

un chien – dog

un chat – cat

un lapin – rabbit

un hamster – hamster

un cochon d'Inde – guinea pig

un cheval – horse

Le corps

The body

JE SUIS MALADE.
I AM ILL.

la tête
head

l'oeil/les yeux
eye/eyes

l'oreille
ear

la bouche
mouth

la dent
tooth

le bras
arm

la poitrine
chest

la main
hand

la jambe
leg

J'AI MAL
À LA MAIN.
MY HAND IS
HURTING.

le pied
foot

GET IT?

J'ai mal… means
'My… hurts'.

J'AI MAL À LA JAMBE.
MY LEG IS HURTING.

Read the conversation between the doctor and the patient.

LE MÉDECIN

OÙ EST-CE QUE VOUS AVEZ MAL?
WHERE DOES IT HURT?

ICI!
HERE!

OUVRE LA BOUCHE.
OPEN YOUR MOUTH.

RESPIRE PROFONDÉMENT.
BREATHE DEEPLY.

CE MÉDICAMENT EST TRÈS BON.
THIS MEDICINE IS VERY GOOD.

Read the labels below.

These are items you can buy from the chemist – **la pharmacie.**

un sparadrap a plaster	**un pansement** a bandage	**une bouteille de médicament** a bottle of medicine	**un comprimé** a tablet

1 euro	*2 euros*	*3 euros*	*1 euro*

In French, write the total cost in euros for the items you bought at the chemist.
The first one has been done for you.

You bought...	Total cost
trois sparadraps et un pansement	cinq euros
quatre pansements et quatre sparadraps	
sept comprimés et une bouteille de médicament	
deux bouteilles de médicament	

Au marché

At the market

VOUS DÉSIREZ?
WHAT WOULD YOU LIKE?

JE VOUDRAIS...
I WOULD LIKE...

une baguette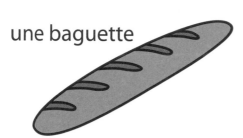

des tomates

des fraises

des poires

des oranges

des po __ __ es

des œu __ __

des caro __ __ es

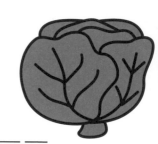

un gâteau

un ch __ __

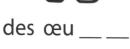
du fromage

un oignon

un poi __ __ on

Complete the word labels next to the food.
Choose from these missing letters.

tt   mm   fs   ou   ss

Combien en voulez-vous?

How much would you like?

Fill in the missing words. Choose from the following:

| lait | fromage | haricots verts | pain | beurre | tomates |

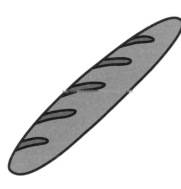

du _____
some bread

un morceau de _____
a piece of cheese

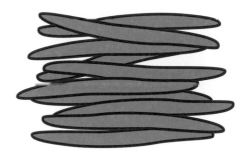

un kilo de _____
green beans

un litre de _____
a litre of milk

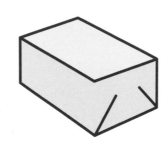

un kilo de _____
a kilo of butter

dix _____
ten tomatoes

C'EST TOUT?
IS THAT ALL?

OUI, C'EST TOUT, MERCI.
YES, NOTHING ELSE, THANKS.

GET IT?
Don't forget to say 'please' (s'il vous plaît) and 'thank you very much' (merci beaucoup)!

USE A FRENCH DICTIONARY FOR ANY WORDS YOU DON'T KNOW.

Le restaurant

The restaurant

Read the snippets of dialogue between the customer and the waiter.

UNE TABLE POUR DEUX PERSONNES, S'IL VOUS PLAÎT.
A TABLE FOR TWO PEOPLE, PLEASE.

LE MENU, S'IL VOUS PLAÎT.
THE MENU, PLEASE.

JE VOUDRAIS LA SOUPE.
I'D LIKE THE SOUP.

L'ADDITION, S'IL VOUS PLAÎT.
THE BILL, PLEASE.

BON APPÉTIT!
ENJOY YOUR MEAL!

GARÇON!
WAITER!

Draw a line from each word to the correct item. Use a French dictionary if you need to.

| une cuillère   un couteau   une fourchette   un verre   une assiette |

une _ _ _ _ _ _ _ _ _ _

un _ _ _ _ _ _ _ _

une _ _ _ _ _ _ _ _ _ _ _

un _ _ _ _ _

une _ _ _ _ _ _ _ _

Read the menu.

Le menu du jour

menu of the day

Soupes – *soups*
soupe à l'oignon – *onion soup*

soupe de poireaux – *leek soup*

Viandes – *meat*
poulet – *chicken*

agneau – *lamb*

bifteck – *steak*

Poissons – *fish*
saumon – *salmon*

truite – *trout*

Omelette – *omelette*

Légumes – *vegetables*
petits pois – *peas*

champignons – *mushrooms*

frites – *fries*

Desserts – *desserts*
glace à la vanille – *vanilla ice cream*

Boissons *drinks*
eau minérale – *mineral water*

jus de fruit – *fruit juice*

café – *coffee*

Try to read this conversation between the waiter and the customer:

1 POUR COMMENCER, UNE SOUPE À L'OIGNON, S'IL VOUS PLAÎT.

3 JE PRENDS LE SAUMON, S'IL VOUS PLAÎT.

2 ET LE PLAT PRINCIPAL?

5 EAU MINÉRALE, S'IL VOUS PLAÎT.

4 ET COMME BOISSON?

GET IT?
Pour commencer … For starter …

Et le plat principal? And for main course?

Et comme boisson? And to drink?

Verbes

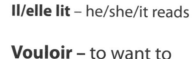

Verbs

Parler – to speak
Je parle – I speak
Il/elle parle – he/she/it speaks

Jouer – to play
Je joue – I play
Il/elle joue – he/she/it plays

Se réveiller – to wake up
Je me réveille – I wake up
Il/elle se réveille – he/she/it wakes up

Lire – to read
Je lis – I read
Il/elle lit – he/she/it reads

Vouloir – to want to
Je veux – I want
Il/elle veut – he/she/it wants

Habiter – to live
J'habite – I live
Il/elle habite – he/she/it lives

Faire – to do
Je fais – I do
Il/elle fait – he/she/it does

Pouvoir – to be able to
Je peux – I can
Il/elle peut – he/she/it can

JE ME RÉVEILLE À SEPT HEURES ET DEMIE.
I GET UP AT 7.30.

JE NE PEUX PAS!
I CAN'T!

Penser – to think
Je pense – I think
Il/elle pense – he/she/it thinks

Aimer – to like
J'aime – I like
Il/elle aime – he/she/it likes

Comprendre – to understand
Je comprends – I understand
Il/elle comprend – he/she/it understands

More useful verbs to learn.

Dormir – to sleep
Je dors – I sleep
Il/elle dort – he/she/it sleeps

Écrire – to write
J'écris – I write
Il/elle écrit – he/she/it writes

Aller – to go
Je vais – I go
Il/elle va – he/she/it goes

Sortir – to go out
Je sors – I go out
Il/elle sort – he/she/it goes out

Join the French to the English translation.

Je vais au cinéma.	I live in London.
Je joue au parc.	I go out with my friends.
J'habite à Londres.	I go to the cinema.
Je sors avec mes amis.	I play in the park.

Answers

Nombres
9 – **neuf**
15 – **quinze**
28 – **vingt-huit**
36 – **trente-six**
70 – **soixante-dix**

2 – **deux**
11 – **onze**
31 – **trente et un**
49 – **quarante-neuf**
80 – **quatre-vingts**

Les vêtements

Mois de l'année
20th May – **le vingt mai**
Christmas Day – **le vingt-cinq décembre**
New Year's Day – **le premier janvier**

Les heures

 Il est six heures.

 Il est deux heures et demie.

 Il est cinq heures et quart.

 Il est huit heures moins le quart.

 Il est neuf heures.

 Il est dix heures et demie.

Contraires

La famille

1. Je m'appelle Michel. J'ai trente ans.
2. Ma mère s'appelle Sylvie.
3. Mon père s'appelle Pascal.
4. Ma sœur s'appelle Clara.
5. Clara a vingt-cinq ans.
6. Ma nièce, Chloé, a deux ans.

Le corps

You bought…	Total cost
trois sparadraps et un pansement	cinq euros
quatre pansements et quatre sparadraps	douze euros
sept comprimés et une bouteille de médicament	dix euros
deux bouteilles de médicament	six euros

Au marché
des caro**tt**es
des po**mm**es
un ch**ou**
un poi**ss**on
des œu**fs**

Combien en voulez-vous?
du pain
un morceau de fromage
un kilo de haricots verts
un litre de lait
un kilo de beurre
dix tomates

Le restaurant
une cuillère – spoon
un couteau – knife
une fourchette – fork
un verre – glass
une assiette – plate

Verbes
Je vais au cinéma.
I go to the cinema.

Je joue au parc.
I play in the park.

J'habite à Londres.
I live in London.

Je sors avec mes amis.
I go out with my friends.